My Story

My Story

The Guide to
Writing Your Book

www.writemystory.co.uk

headline

First published in 2008

by HEADLINE PUBLISHING GROUP

1

Cataloguing in Publication Data is available from the British Library

ISBN 978 07553 1774 5

Design by Ben Cracknell Studios

Cover design by Hello!Lucky

Printed and bound in Great Britain by Mackays of Chatham plc

Headline's policy is to use papers that are natural, renewable and recyclable products and made from wood grown in sustainable forests. The logging and manufacturing processes are expected to conform to the environmental regulations of the country of origin.

HEADLINE PUBLISHING GROUP

An Hachette Livre UK Company
338 Euston Road
London NW1 3BH

www.headline.co.uk

Contents

Introduction

> 'You see things; and you say, "Why?" But I
> dream things that never were; and I say,
> "Why not?"'   *George Bernard Shaw*

In front of you is a blank book waiting to be filled
with your story. This guide is here to help you. It is
just that: a guide and not an instruction manual. You
don't have to start where suggested, you don't have to
tackle all the sections and you certainly don't have to
follow all the prompts. They're called prompts rather
than questions because they're here to help you and not
to challenge you.

Some of the prompts are merely matters of fact: 'my
grandparents', 'occupations' or 'places I have worked'.
Others require you to arrive at a judgment rather than
just recall a fact: 'friends I regret losing' or 'what I, as an
adult, would want to tell my eleven-year-old self'.
Prompts like these encourage you to reflect on your life.
There will be bad times as well as good times to recall,
but if this is to be a true record of your life then the

possibility of wistfulness is a risk worth taking. The key thing to remember is that this is a book of your *whole* life and not a diary. It's about words and thoughts, memories and feelings – not just facts and figures. And that means thinking not only about your birth, childhood and adult life, but also about your death: from songs you would want to be played at your funeral to the inscription you would like on your tombstone and precisely how – and perhaps even when – you wish to be remembered.

My Story offers a unique and indispensable testament to your life. It gives you the chance to record all your thoughts about life in general and your life in particular. This will be the book you leave behind – for your nearest and dearest and those that come afterwards. Alternatively, you can keep it secret and take it with you to the grave. It's up to you.

You can write in the book by hand – perhaps leaving spaces for updates – or you can use a computer and print out the pages to stick them in the book. Again, that's your decision. Go online and discover the website **www.writemystory.co.uk**, which enables you to communicate with other readers and to share the feelings – good and bad – that you've experienced.

My Story is a keepsake, a log book, a testament that isn't a will. Above all, it's yours for you to write as you see fit. It's your story and it's as unique as you are.

My Birth

Like any organisation, families are in a constant state of flux: your birth crystallises your family in a precise moment of time. What did *you* bring to your family?

Find out about your earliest experiences when you were born – not merely the date and time and how much you weighed, which is all most of us are actually told.

Speak to those who witnessed your earliest days – if that is still possible. Contact your parents, aunts, grandparents and any brothers and sisters who were around at the time. Tell them about the book you're writing and ask for their co-operation. Perhaps sharing memories will prompt them to start writing their own life story.

Try not to take too much notice of hearsay – second-hand remarks such as, 'Your grandmother used to say you were a very hungry baby.' If your grandmother is still alive, go and ask her.

Compiling this book may at times be delicate and even painful. It may cause anger, tears and even rows. Some people, especially older generations, prefer to leave their emotions and the past buried. So, as you delve into your past, you will almost certainly release skeletons from cupboards to which others might have preferred to throw away the key. So you may encounter people who simply don't want to talk about it, but try to leave no stone unturned in the quest for your story. It will be worth it.

- **Approximate date of conception – work it out!**

- **Place of conception. Don't be embarrassed to ask your parents.**

- **Date of birth. Were you 'late' or 'early'?**

- **Day of birth. See website for perpetual calendar.**

- **Place of birth: town, home and hospital.**

- **People present at my birth: midwife/doctors, friends/family.**

- **Type of birth. Was it natural or caesarean?**

- **Duration of labour.**

- **Birth complications. What pain relief – if any – did your mother use?**

- Star sign/rising sign. See website.

- Birthstone. See website.

- Other people born on the same day as you. See website to see which celebrity/celebrities shares your birthday.

- All about the day you were born: the weather, the number one song, books in the shops, films at the cinema, etc. See website.

- Key things that happened in the year you were born. See website.

- How/why your name was chosen.

- What your name means. See website.

- Your parents' ambitions for you before your birth. Before your parents even met you, they will have had many thoughts about you and plans for you. Were you a long awaited son/daughter?

- Family circumstances surrounding your birth. What was the state of your family at the time of your birth? Was everyone's health good or was your birth a welcome distraction from the problems of your (great)grandparents?

- What you were like as a small baby. Did you sleep? Did you cry a lot? Were you easy to feed? Were you breastfed? Did you put on weight easily? Were you a fast developer, or did you do everything in your own good time?

- The effect of your birth on your parents and family.

- Your earliest memories.

My Family

'In the end, it always comes down to
family. Forget everything else – fame,
money, work – that's what matters.'

Sir Michael Caine

The family is the framework within which our lives are contained and your parents have the huge responsibility of directing and shaping your life until you are able to leave the nest and choose the people with whom you want to share your life.

Perhaps you were an only child or lost a sibling through death or divorce? If you had siblings, they might have had contrasting and conflicting experiences to your own – perhaps because your parents were wealthier/poorer at key stages of your lives. This might explain your different approaches to work, spending, giving and indeed all money-related issues throughout your life.

Perhaps you (or they) were the favourite or the scapegoat for all the family's ills? Your position in the family –

where you came or whether you were an only child – will impact on your upbringing and the person you are today.

The eldest and the youngest in any family tend to have different characteristics to the others: the eldest might have been obliged to shoulder more responsibility and might have been subjected to stricter rules, while the youngest, as the baby of the family, might have been indulged. Has this pattern continued into adulthood?

Then there are all the extraneous family factors such as illness, disability, unemployment, death, etc., that shape our lives. By far the most common of these is divorce, which reshapes families and affects individuals by creating extended families and any number of potential familial and emotional hazards. People take sides, loyalties are divided and sensitivities are hardened. Many children are affected by divorce, but what matters here is how *you* were affected. Perhaps it was the best thing your parents could have done in the circumstances.

- Your basic family tree template. See website.

- Your parents: their names and dates of birth.

- Your parents' occupation(s) before marriage and during it. If your mother was a housewife, did she have any aspirations/regrets?

- Your parents' temperament. Were they strict/kind/indulgent?

- Your parents' relationship with each other. Were they happy?

- Your grandparents: their names and dates/places of birth.

- Your grandparents' occupation.

- Your grandparents' standard of living. How well-off/poor were they?

- How your grandparents influenced your parents. Were they strict or religious?

- How your grandparents influenced you. Maybe they lived with you or helped look after you?

- Your great-grandparents: names, occupations and origins. Ask as many relatives are you can. What did they look like?

- Your aunts/uncles: names, occupations and closeness to your own parents.

- Your cousins: names and details. The more they can tell you about their parents and your shared grandparents, the better.

- Your siblings: names and dates of birth. How close in age and outlook were you? All siblings fight but were there any lasting conflicts?

- How your parents treated them. Did their attitude differ towards you?

- Your relationship with your siblings as adults. Are you close?

- Your godparents, if you have any. How were they chosen? How involved have they been in your life?

- Your place in the order of the family. Did you and your siblings have allocated chores? Did you have designated seats around the table and in the lounge?

- Your role in the family: linchpin/scapegoat/peacemaker/fixer/black sheep?

- What made your family different from others: religion/politics/hobbies?

- Your family secrets – or rumours? Include things you've heard but never investigated.

- Your family rows. What characterised yours? Was one of you a stirrer or tell-tale or sneak? Who tended to start – and finish – them? What was the aftermath like?

- Your peacemaker. Did you have one?

- Your inherited family traits/tendencies. Do/did you follow in anyone's footsteps?

- Your family disputes/disasters. Have you ever broken off all contact with a relative? If so, for how long and how was it made up?

- Your relationship with your family now.

- Your contribution to your family. How much did you do around the house? Who did the washing-up? Did you pay rent when you started working? Were you generous to your family with money/presents/time? When you left home, did you ever help family members financially, or did you give them your time rather than your money?

- Your family's finances. How wealthy was your family? Was your family wealthier or poorer than your extended family? Did your family's wealth fluctuate? Was money inherited? Was money ever used as a means of control?

- Your family meals/menus. What were your mother's best dishes and what were her worst? Was there a rota? Was there a choice? To what extent have your current eating habits been influenced by meals eaten as a child? Was food/the family meal important to you and your family, or was it something to be endured?

- Your family traditions. How were special events celebrated?

- Did you celebrate Christmas or other religious festivals? What was the day like in your house? With which members of your extended family did you spend it? Was it always the same?

- **Your birthdays.** Are there any presents you particularly remember receiving or not receiving?

- **Your family weddings and other celebrations:** dates and details.

- **Your family funerals:** dates, details and any special facts you remember about these occasions. Did anything funny happen to lighten the mood?

My Homes

'Home is a place you grow up wanting to leave, and grow old wanting to get back to.'

John Ed Pearce

Where you're brought up has a huge impact on how you grow up. The ideal is a comfortable house with a garden in a safe area and plenty of space to play in, but not everyone has that luxury. Maybe you were born into hardship, or in a developing country, a country with a weak economy or during a war. Family fortunes can change. Parents can be promoted/made redundant/decide on a job change that involves moving home.

When you become an adult, you want your own place but the expense and responsibility that this entails sometimes drives people back to the family nest, not least because the only place you can initially afford is likely to be less appealing than the home you were trying to escape.

Then there's property price inflation, which forces more and more young people to live with their parents or to share increasingly large mortgage repayments with friends or even strangers. Once on the property ladder, many people find that they move on a regular basis, trading up at every opportunity, until they find their dream home – or the best home they can afford. However, there are three things that can interfere with the best-laid plans: death, divorce and debt.

Here is where you can chronicle all the homes you have lived in from when you were a baby, how long you lived there, what you liked or disliked about them and why you moved.

If possible try to find out how much the homes cost to buy, how much they were sold for and anything that quantifies how much those homes (or similar ones) cost today (see website). It is amazing, for example, that you could buy a large flat in central London for £10,000 as recently as the 1970s.

- **Your first home. If possible, ask your parents – or perhaps an older sibling – for details. What was your bedroom like? Did you share with your parents or have one of your own?**

- Your first proper bedroom. Did you have to share with a sibling?

- Your sibling(s)' bedroom. Did you covet theirs?

- Decoration. Did you choose or did your parents choose?

- Your parents' room(s). Was there a 'best' room/a room for grown-ups only?

- Your parents' attitude to housekeeping. Was yours a show home or was it cluttered but comfortable?

- Your gardens. What were they like? What games did you play? Which friends did you entertain?

- Removal days. Can you remember moving house? Did you help or were you bundled out of the way? How did you feel about moving? Did you lose touch with friends?

- Your refuge from home. When it all got too much to bear, where did you go? Was there a member of your extended family or a friend's family who would look after you when you had trouble at home? Did your parents know about this refuge and, if so, how did they respond to it?

- Your street/neighbours/park.

- Your town/village/suburb.

- Your first home away from home. Were you homesick? How and why did you choose it?

- Your first family/marital home.

- Your subsequent homes. Prepare a list detailing when/why you moved and the prices/rents of those homes. Rate them in order of preference.

- Your holiday homes as a child and as an adult. Did you have a caravan, a boat?

- Home improvements: best and worst.

- Your dream home. What would it be like? Or are you already in it?

My Education

You grow up being told that 'schooldays are the best days of your life' and that can fill you with fear: if these really are the best days of our lives, then how bad could the rest turn out to be? For some people schooldays are a wonderful opportunity for self-expression, learning and understanding; a time for forging lifelong friendships and amassing trophies and certificates. For others, schooldays can be a miserable time of feeling inadequate, unsuccessful and being bullied.

It is a matter of luck where you go to school, and depends on any number of factors beyond your control including your parents' financial situation, where you live and perhaps how much your parents value education. It's also a matter of luck who else is there when you get there. Even if you are fortunate enough to go to a fabulous school – whether it has enviable facilities or an outstanding academic track record – you can have the bad luck to fall foul of a particular teacher or fellow pupil. Two siblings at the same school can have completely contrasting experiences.

Sometimes it's your own fault. As you assemble your life stories, you may find that you can pinpoint the moment in your school career when it started to go wrong. Perhaps when you picked the wrong friend, when you were off school for most of a term due to illness, or even when you became too successful and made yourself unpopular.

This is the place for you to chronicle your experiences, to note down your recollections of your schools.

And what if you could go back, knowing what you've learned since, and do it all again? Would you make the same mistakes? Was there any word or advice, perhaps from a teacher, that you now wish you'd heeded? Was there a friend you wish you had dropped – or one that you really wish you'd made? What would you say now to the teacher you disliked the most?

- **All the schools you attended, including dates and addresses and updated names.**

- **Your favourite/least favourite school.**

- **Your favourite/least favourite teachers.**

- Your favourite/least favourite subjects.

- The school you wish you had attended.

- Achievements.

- Prizes.

- Punishments and discipline.

- How you got to and from school: school bus/public transport. How much did it cost? Did you walk or cycle, or did you get lifts from a parent? Was this done willingly?

- School trips: good and bad.

- School dinners: cost, quality and things on the menu you most/least liked.

- Uniforms. Were they optional or compulsory? Strict or relaxed?

- Most hated piece of uniform or kit.

- Sports Day. Was it your favourite or worst day of the year?

- School plays/choir. Did you take part? Or did you do your best to avoid them?

- Your best friends in each school.

- Your worst enemies in each school.

- The people who bullied you.

- The person/people who protected you from bullies.

- The people you bullied or were unpleasant to.

- School rules. Did you break them? What were the punishments? Who administered them?

- Memories: good and bad.

- What happened to your schoolmates? Did any of them end up as big successes or, indeed, as huge failures?

- School reports. How good were yours? Did you hide them from your parents?

- Regrets about the schools you did attend and those you didn't.

- What you would tell your eight-year-old self.

- What you would tell your teenage self.

My Childhood

'When I was a boy of fourteen, my father
was so ignorant I could hardly stand to
have the old man around. But when I got
to twenty-one, I was astonished at how
much he had learned in seven years.'

Mark Twain

During your childhood years your character
forms and your personality develops.
Friendships – some of them lifelong – are
made. Habits and pastimes begin and a way of life is
established.

Try to record the key elements of your childhood: your
whole life out of school. Were these happy, contented
years or did you find growing up a constant challenge?
When you look back at your childhood, it's often
through rose-tinted spectacles. Now is the time to take
them off.

Out of school, you may have taken up an absorbing hobby or sport – or maybe you had a bike and used it to meet up with your friends. What attracted you to those friends? Were they merely neighbours or was there something else that bound you together? What did you do together? In what way(s) did those relationships help to make you the person you are today?

Think about the formative events that shaped your childhood: some of them will have seemed important even at the time but some will only have become so in retrospect.

Were there things you neglected to do in your childhood – like rolling down a grassy hill, painting with your hands, climbing a tree or flying a kite?

Think back to the high days when the sun was always shining and summer went on for ever and also to the low, angst-ridden days when you wondered how you would ever face the next day? What were the cataclysmic events of your childhood, or were there none? Was life uneventful and dull? If so, how did that affect you? Perhaps you couldn't wait to leave home? Or school?

Did your family stay together, or fragment? Did your parents split up and remarry? If so, how, why and when? And how did you get on with your parents during these formative years? Were they always there for you? Or were you left to fend for yourself?

Were you well? Or were there illnesses? Maybe you struggled with asthma or suffered from panic attacks. Perhaps you worried about your looks or your weight. How did you feel about yourself?

- Your friends in addition to your school friends.

- Holidays and holiday jobs.

- Hobbies you had, including hobbies you tried but dropped.

- Bicycles.

- Possessions.

- Favourite toys.

- Favourite games.

- Favourite books/comics.

- Favourite TV programmes.

- Favourite sports.

- Favourite sweets and chocolates.

- Hang-outs.

- Serious illnesses, including operations.

- Pin-ups.

- Your clubs and societies. Were you a scout or a guide?

- Sports teams you supported.

- Sporting heroes/heroines.

- Musical instruments played, and to what level.

- Musical instruments abandoned and why.

- Your favourite music in childhood, including all the songs you feel embarrassed about now.

- Your most influential role models.

- Deaths of relatives and childhood friends or acquaintances. Include those that affected you most and those that should have but perhaps didn't.

- People you knew who grew up to be famous/notorious.

- The people who looked after you: doctors, dentists, babysitters.

- I wish I hadn't done it…

- When you first heard about sex.

- Your biggest lie/misdemeanour.

- The most hurtful thing you ever said to anyone.

My Working Life

What you do/did for a living defines you – to yourself as well as to others – almost more than anything else you do in life. When recording your working life try to ensure that you don't simply create a CV of achievements and positions held. The most significant time spent at work will almost certainly have nothing to do with the job itself: it's the people you work with – and for – who help to shape your career and character.

Take this opportunity to really think about what your job(s) have meant to you. Has your working life simply been a question of earning money or was there a social or vocational element to your endeavours as well? And was this fulfilled?

Did you work to live or did you live to work? Did you enjoy work or hate it? Think too of the effect of your working life on your family life and on your relationships with friends and lovers. Did you have to leave the parental home when you entered the workplace, or did you stay until you had really found your feet financially? What did you contribute to the family finances and family life generally?

When you're considering your career, think too about the effect of any dismissals or redundancies. These will have felt awful at the time but sometimes they will have turned out to be blessings in disguise. Setbacks are the price you pay for wisdom and you learn far more from the things that go wrong than the things that turn out just as you planned.

Also take time to think about the months and even years when you weren't working, including unemployment. They are part of the light and shade of your working life, too.

- Your youthful ambition.

- Further education and qualifications.

- Leaving home. Date and reason and your strongest memories of how you felt: excited/nervous/ worried/elated/relieved?

- First job(s). How and why you chose it or they chose you.

- First boss: name and age and general description. Did you like him or her?

- Journeys to work: cost and description. Was travel subsidised or provided? Or did you commute and spend time and money?

- Best/worst workmates: names, personalities and how you related to them.

- Best job(s): reason you took it/them and reason you left.

- Worst job(s): how long they lasted and how much you were paid. Why was it so awful?

- Job you should have taken and reasons why it didn't happen.

- Job you shouldn't have taken and why you did.

- What you wish you had said to your boss, whether generally or on a specific occasion(s).

- Office relationships. Were these good or bad or encouraged or dominant?

- Workplace romances. Did you indulge?

- Fun at work, including outings and parties.

- Major career influences: role models or personal contacts.

- Your mentor and people who helped you through hard times.

- The day you were sacked or made redundant, or the day you resigned.

- People responsible for where you are today.

- Promotions/demotions you deserved/didn't deserve.

- Why you had to leave jobs.

- Your youthful ambition.

- The career you wish you'd chosen.

- The greatest wrong ever done to you in the workplace.

- My best and worst paid jobs.

My Holidays and Travel

'The whole object of travel is not to set
foot on foreign land; it is at last to set foot
on one's own country as a foreign land.'

G.K. Chesterton

S ome people spend all their available income on travel while others have never been remotely tempted to leave the country they were born in. Sometimes, you travel the world in search of what you need and don't find it till you return home. Sometimes it's only when you're away from home that you get any sense of perspective about your life at home. Holidays and travel — and they're sometimes very different things — enable you to explore the world and also yourself. Where you go to — the type of holidays you choose — should give you some important insights into who you are.

But it needn't be so profound: holidays and travel can also simply provide the much-needed counter-balance to the daily routine that simultaneously drives you and imprisons you.

It starts in childhood with the holidays you enjoy/endure with your family. To what extent have those experiences coloured your approach to holidays in your adult life? Ask yourself what function holidays and travel serve in your life. Are they about a break or a respite from work? Or do you have a hankering to discover?

In other words, some of us travel to escape and some of us travel to seek – while others do both. Which 'camp' you find yourself in can be very telling when you're assessing your life.

Holidays also provide us with the opportunity to bond with existing friends and to make new ones. Indeed, some of us judge the success of our holidays on the strength of those friendships. Remembering and analysing both types of friendship will help you enormously when you come to the section on people (see p. 39).

- **Countries you have been to. List them and the dates you were there.**

- **Countries you still want to visit, perhaps in order of most wanted.**

- **Countries you would never visit/revisit and why.**

- People you have holidayed/travelled with. Did you return closer or did you have (terminal) bust-ups with them?

- People you have met on your travels.

- Famous landmarks you have seen. Did they live up to your expectations?

- Famous landmarks or places you hope to explore.

- Places you wish you had visited when you were younger.

- Trips that changed your life – for better or worse.

- Holiday romances. Did you make any lasting relationships? Or break them? Do you regret any of them?

- Your special place.

- Thrilling moments, including adventures and pursuits.

- Things you would still like to do on holiday.

- Dreadful moments: illnesses, lost luggage, a stolen passport, horribly delayed flights, trouble with immigration or the police.

- The holiday you would return to if you could go back in time.

- Best holiday.

- **Worst holiday.**

- **Your favourite hotel.**

- **Your least favourite hotel.**

- **Your favourite weekend destination.**

- **Your most expensive mistake.**

- **Your biggest cultural blunder.**

My Friends

'Anybody can sympathise with the
sufferings of a friend, but it requires a very
fine nature to sympathise with a friend's
success.'
Oscar Wilde

From the day you are born you start collecting
people around you. The family you arrive in, the
friends you make, the colleagues you work with
and the neighbours you find yourself living close to.
Then there are the people you meet through your
hobbies and pastimes, all of whom go to make up the
rich tapestry of your life. The people play a huge part in
the time you spend away from work and they help you to
form your views of the world – and of yourself.

Friends hold up the mirror in which you see yourself.
And that's why true friendship is a responsibility as well
as a privilege. Many friends help you to make your way
through difficult times as well as the best times. Often
they surprise you with their support and loyalty. And

sometimes they let you down, ultimately forfeiting your friendship. Letting go is hard and sometimes you may hang on to a friendship out of sentimentality.

Have you lost friends along the way? If so, why? Are there friends you lost but wished you hadn't? Perhaps later events overtook you and a friendship was squandered needlessly. Perhaps other people, jealous of your friendship, came between you and caused trouble?

Look at the friends you have rather than just at the friends you have lost. When evaluating these friends, don't underestimate the complexity of friendship by asking yourself which friend(s) would be there for you in a crisis. There are difficult times when you need your friends to gather round but, the truth is, just as good a test of friendship is how happy a friend is when something has gone well for you. Sometimes you find that you have friends for the good times and friends for the bad times – because different friends have different qualities. Neither is 'better' than the other. But your best friend will be the one who is there for you through both good times and bad.

- **Best friends at different ages.**

- **Best neighbours.**

- **Worst neighbours.**

- **Your enemies. What became of them?**

- Flatmates. How did you choose them? Or was it you who were chosen?

- What you valued most about each friend, e.g., good listener, supportive, calming, entertaining, interesting.

- Friends you have lost through quarrels, moving, illness or death. What do you wish you'd said to them.

- Memorable presents you have given friends or received from them.

- Friends you kept for too long, perhaps out of habit?

- Mistakes you made in friendships. Be honest!

- The fun/silly things you did with friends.

- The worst thing you ever did/said to a friend/enemy.

- The nicest thing anyone ever said to/about you.

- Your rock(s): the friend(s) you can depend on in any circumstance.

- Friends you wish you had made. Were you keener on the friendship than they were?

- Friends you wish you'd kept. How did you lose touch?

My Pets

Different animals appeal to different people.
Some people like tranquil animals like cats,
rabbits and guinea pigs, which require nothing
beyond care and the odd cuddle. Others prefer animals
like dogs and horses, which take them out of the house
and give them exercise. Either way, it's certainly true that
while animals could live without us, it would be almost
impossible to live without animals.

A pet can also become almost a confidant. The fact that
they don't understand the precise meaning of our words
is irrelevant: they understand the mood in which they are
spoken. Did you ever tell an animal something in
confidence to clear your mind? Have you ever wished
that a pet could talk back to you, or even become
human?

Have you ever lost a pet, or nursed one through a terrible illness or injury? Have you ever known a bond so deep you have become inseparable? There are many people who prefer their pets to family or friends. Pets are a great comfort and studies show they not only help to combat stress but can actually prolong life.

Have you acquired a pet that turned into a complete disaster? Perhaps it was very ill and required veterinary services you couldn't afford? Or maybe you rescued a dog that turned out to be extremely disobedient or even vicious? Taking on and maintaining an animal takes a fair amount of responsibility. Do you feel that the pleasure you have had from having pets has outweighed the cost, the time and the commitment?

- **Your first pet.**

- **Other memorable pets in your life.**

- **Pet highlights. What are your favourite memories of each one of your pets?**

- **Pet illnesses and deaths.**

- **Pet regrets. Was there an animal you should never have owned? Was there a specific type of pet you always hankered after? Is there an animal you would never own again?**

- **All the money you have spent on pets.**

- Bad experiences with animals.

- The one pet you would have immortalised if you could.

- Animals you have rescued.

- Animals you wish you could have taken in.

- Friends' pets. Were there any you adored or loathed?

- Animals you feared or were allergic to.

- Pets you have preferred to people. Did a pet ever come between you and a friend or lover?

My Health

Health – or, at least, good health – is one of those things it's easy to take for granted. That's to say, you only notice it when it's gone. Unless, that is, you have been born with a disease or disability that has dominated your entire life.

The day you catch a cold you tell yourself that you would be so happy if only you didn't have a cold, but you know that's not true. Illness is a part of childhood because your immune system is more vulnerable. And even with vaccinations, you get used to being unwell for days, even weeks at a time. Thereafter, illness punctuates life like a gatecrasher at a party. You curse it at the time and yet, without it, you would not have built up the resilience you need to get through life. Your body changes through puberty, pregnancy, the menopause and the ageing process. Maybe you have had physical setbacks: infertility, miscarriages or bouts of debilitating ill health, perhaps caused through work or lifestyle. Perhaps you have learned to live with back pain, migraines or insomnia. Much of your health is inherited and so in compiling this section you will be providing potentially invaluable information for those you leave behind.

Your physical health – and appearance – can also affect your mental health and it's important to chart your mental well-being throughout your life. Many people suffer depression at some stage of life, but there's a huge difference between 'state depression', where you're upset or anxious because of something that's happening – or not happening – in your life and 'trait depression', where you're pre-disposed through your genetic make up to melancholy or anxiety. The important thing is to know yourself.

You are not immune to your environment and cross-checking your (ill) health against where you've lived could prove a useful experience . Chart all your bad habits – like smoking, drug-taking and excessive drinking – in order to help you to understand the significance and the consequences of the abuse you might have done to your body.

It is easy to forget your medical history and medical records can be lost so here is a good place to record your state of health from birth right up to the present day.

- Your operations and serious illnesses. Apply to your doctor's surgery for a copy of your medical records and make notes from those. Ditto your dentist and any complementary practitioners you may have seen.

- Accidents: dates, damage, pain, treatment, recovery. Has there been any long-term damage, either physical or psychological? Did you receive any compensation? Should you have done?

- Familial conditions. Do you have any inherited conditions? Check with (older) relatives to discover any risk factors.

- Your mental well-being. How have you handled stress/anxiety/depression?

- Your blood group. Have you ever received or donated blood?

- Your phobia(s). Is there anything that you fear to an extent that it affects your life?

- Your sleeping patterns. How have these changed?

- The worst night's sleep you ever had.

- Your emotional triggers/pressure points. What are they and who knows how to activate/relieve them?

- What you wish you had known/done in your youth with regard to your health.

- Your smoking history.

- Your drinking habits.

- Your allergies. Include foods and drinks you can't tolerate.

- Your use of (illegal) drugs.

- Your bad habits and how you have tried to conquer them.

- Your dietary history. What foods have proved to be your weaknesses/strengths?

My Appearance

'How things look on the outside of us
depends on how things are on the inside
of us.'   *Anon.*

Some people are relaxed about the way they look,
while others attend to every aspect of their
appearance with great care and are prepared to
spend a lot of money on it. Perhaps you have a personal
relationship with your hairdresser or, alternatively, you
feel that a haircut is simply a necessity like a dental check
up. Some women can't even face their loved ones without
putting on full make up, while others never wear it. The
same diversities apply to wearing fragrances and even
personal hygiene. What's your take on it?

Include photos of yourself at various ages of your life and
add some comments, perhaps saying where the photo
was taken and by whom, and what you were doing,
wearing or thinking at the time. Don't be embarrassed to
include pictures of yourself wearing once-fashionable
clothes that you would no longer consider wearing.

How has your appearance changed with the years? Ask your oldest friends to tell you honestly. Has your figure or physique been an issue for you? What lengths have you gone to in order to look as good as possible? Have you ever followed a weight-loss diet and how successful was it?

How do you see your 'style'? How do others see it? Ask friends to give you their frank assessment. Has your style changed over the years? Have you smartened up your appearance or do you take every opportunity to dress down? Do you dress up for work, or do you wear jeans whenever you can? To what extent do you follow fashion or are you a free spirit who wears what's comfortable and suits your lifestyle?

- What you like about your body.

- What you hate about your body.

- Your body shape. What have you done to change/improve it?

- Temporary and permanent changes you have made to your body – tattoos and piercings, for example.

- Mistakes you have made to/with your body or appearance.

- The changes you would/should have made to your body.

- Your diet and the effect on your body. Has your life/appearance been dominated by food and diets?

- Your eyes and eyesight. Have you worn glasses or contact lenses? Have you had laser surgery? Would you consider it?

- Your hair. How has your hairstyle changed over the years? How much have you spent on it? What has been your best/worst hairstyle?

- Your personal hygiene routine. Bath or shower? How has this changed over the years?

- Your teeth. How many fillings have you had? What is your dental record?

- Your skin. Is it ageing well? What do you do to protect it and enhance it?

- Personal grooming. What's your routine? How has it changed over the years?

- Your hands. Do you bite your nails? How do you look after your hands and nails?

- Your feet. What care do you take of your feet? Do you hide them or do you take every opportunity to display them?

- You and the sun. Do you sunbathe? What protection do you use? How has this changed over the years? Do you use tanning parlours?

- Your marks/birthmarks. Do you have any? Have they changed shape?

- Beauty treatments. What do you use? Have available treatments changed over the years?

- Your style. How would you describe it? How would your friends describe it? How has it changed? How much do you spend on clothes annually?

- Your favourite outfit(s), both now and in the past.

- Shoes and boots. Are they a weakness or do you tend to buy one pair and wear them out?

- Handbags, purses and wallets. What do you use? Do you spend a lot of money on them or do you look for something functional?

- Jewellery and watches. What are your favourite pieces? Is there any significance to what you wear? What would you most like to own?

- Other accessories. List your favourite hats, scarves, sunglasses, briefcases and other accessories. Why are they so special to you?

- Outerwear. Do you wear jackets or overcoats, or do you prefer just to wear jumpers in winter? Do you, or would you, wear fur?

- Your favourite fragrance. How has this changed over the years? Make a list.

- Your extravagances and indulgences when you need a treat. Facials? Makeovers?

- Nightwear. How has this changed over the years?

- Underwear. Do you go for sturdy basics or designer knickers? Do you make your choice to impress or for comfort?

- Favourite shops.

- Favourite designers.

- Best bargain you ever bought. What happened to it?

- Most extravagant mistake.

- Worst thing you ever wore.

- Your wedding dress or suit. Were you happy with the choice and the effect?

- The oldest thing in your wardrobe. Why haven't you chucked it out?

My Finances

'When someone says, "it's not the money, it's the principle", nine times out of ten it's the money.' *Murphy's Law*

There's a saying that there's more to life than money – and so there is – but there's no doubting its importance: especially when you don't have enough of it. Lack of money can lead to unhappiness, suffering and marital discord. And yet too much money can be equally harmful: look at how many lottery winners find their lives blighted by it. That's because when you don't have money, you project all your problems on to what you lack. As soon as the financial problem is resolved, the problems are thrown into sharp relief.

We are born into families that may be rich, poor, or – in most cases in the western world – somewhere in between. Some people, even rich people, go through their entire lives wanting more than they could ever need.

Most people at some stage have dreamed of what they'd do if they were left a lot of money or won a lot of money. How would you have spent your imaginary inheritance or winnings when you were younger, and how would you spend it now? Is there a difference in priorities over the years? Has lack of money stopped you from doing things or did you somehow find a way of doing what you wanted to do anyway?

Your relationship with money will have had an important effect on your whole life. It might have caused rifts in friendships and relationships. Is money your master or your servant? Does money – and the acquisition of money – dominate your life? Or do you feel that money, although useful, is a tool and not something that will cure all your problems?

- **Pocket money through your childhood. How much did it buy at the time? See website.**

- **Money received from relatives. Was it only on birthdays and at Christmas or did they also give you money at other times?**

- **First income/wage packet. Was it earned by having a Saturday job or a holiday job? If so, how much did you get in your first 'proper' job?**

- **First major purchase made with your 'own' money.**

- Your family's attitude to money. Were your parents 'careful', frugal or perhaps even mean? Or were they relaxed, maybe even slapdash? Did your parents discuss money with you?

- Money you came by dishonestly. Did you help yourself to money that was lying around the family home? Or worse, someone else's home or school? What did you do with it?

- Time(s) you sacrificed happiness for money. Have you ever denied yourself things in order to save? Have you ever done anything you didn't want to/shouldn't have done just for the money?

- Gambling. Are you/were you a gambler? Was one of your family? What effect has gambling had on your life?

- Your biggest gamble/bet. What's the most (as a percentage of your overall wealth) you've ever staked or won? Has a close friend or sibling won or lost so much money that it has affected your relationship with them?

- Your biggest debt. Not just in size but also in scope, as a percentage of your overall wealth at the time.

- Your first mortgage. How much was it, what rate of interest did you pay and how easy was it to afford? Did anyone help you with the deposit?

- Subsequent mortgages, remortgages and loans.

- Your greatest extravagance, past and present. Did you enjoy it? Did you feel guilty about it?

- Money inherited. What was it worth then/now? Do you have any 'expectations' in the future?

- All the cars you have bought. How much did you pay and what did you get when you sold them?

- Your pet meanness(es). Where do you like to make economies? How do you feel about other people's meanness?

- Money lent and money borrowed. Have there been any consequences?

- Your attitude to tipping. Have you ever refused to tip? What's the most lavish tip you've ever given? Do you give money to people on the streets?

- What would you buy if money were no object – indulge yourself here...

My Relationships:
Love and Marriage

'Any marriage, happy or unhappy, is
infinitely more interesting than any
romance, however passionate.' *W.H. Auden*

Most of us spend our lives in the pursuit and the fulfilment of love. Along the way there are huge highs and massive lows. Looking back, you wouldn't have missed a single moment – or would you? Were there moments you wish had never happened or people you wish you'd never met and got involved with?

If you're now married or committed to someone, how do you view those times? With pride? With regret? With wistfulness? With marvel and gratitude?

Take the opportunity to look anew at the people who have loved you and whom you have loved – even if the two groups didn't always neatly coincide, or last the test of time. Timing is a key factor and maybe you met the right person at the wrong time or, worse, the wrong person at the right time… Are there factors that have repeated themselves throughout and, if so, how damaging have they been? Think about lost love: failed relationships, although painful at the time, can help us to grow and develop, to the benefit of future relationships. Take the time to celebrate all the love in your life. Where you met, those magical moments when you fell in love, the terrible times when you realised the relationship was over – and why.

Cast your mind back to the person you were before you settled down and to the person you're with: look at your progress together. Chronicle your relationship(s) and see how you shaped them and, more importantly, how they shaped you.

- **The day you lost your virginity. How did you feel before, and how did you feel afterwards? What happened to that first lover?**

- **Your subsequent sexual partners. What do you think about them now?**

- **The one(s) you regret(ted). What made you succumb to their charms?**

- **The one(s) that got away. Whatever happened to them?**

- Your best lover.

- Your worst lover.

- The love of your life.

- Your greatest/worst dates. What characterised them?

- The day you met your current/last partner. Recall everything you can about your first meeting: who else was there, what you said to each other and what you thought about him or her on your first meeting.

- Your first impressions of people you have loved: how accurate were they as you came to know them?

- Relationship milestones in your most important relationship or marriage.

- Your partner's sexual history. Do you discuss it?

- Your partner's family. How welcoming have they been?

- Your sexual fantasy.

- Your sexual hang-ups or fears.

- How your sex life has changed over the years. Is this a cause for regret? Or has it got better with age?

- Gay experiences. Regrets? Opportunities?

- **What you love/like most about your partner.**

- **What you hate/dislike most about your partner.**

- **Your thoughts about your present relationship.**

- **Your thoughts about your future love life.**

My Children and Grandchildren

Before family planning, whether or not you had children was entirely down to Mother Nature. Some people had more than they could cope with, while others found themselves childless.

Now, thanks to the pill on the one hand and IVF on the other, many people have the precise number of children they want. But there can still be a degree of uncertainty about the size of your family. Unplanned births change and sometimes fracture families. Were your children planned or were they 'mistakes'? How has this affected you and how has it affected them?

Increasingly, some people are choosing to be childless, but even they are rarely without nieces, nephews and/or godchildren, which means that they too have a stake in the next generation.

Or perhaps you chose to adopt children, or offer them a temporary home as a foster parent?

Nevertheless, however much control it's now possible to have over fertility, compared with only a couple of generations ago, you may still end up with regrets. Perhaps your children didn't turn out as you had hoped and expected; perhaps your decision not to have children was one you came to regret.

Even if, as a parent, you're delighted with your children and the way they've developed, there is still plenty of scope for heartache and pain. Every setback your child encounters makes you ache – especially if your intervention would only make things worse. Your head tells you that they have to overcome obstacles on their own but your heart prompts you to rush to their aid: how you reconcile those two conflicting forces goes a long way to characterising your approach to parenthood.

Grandchildren are usually a less complicated source of pleasure because grandparents can enjoy all the aspects of parenthood without the ultimate responsibility. Do you agree? Or have you had to take charge more than you would have wished? Do you get on with your child's spouse/partner? Is access to your grandchild(ren) a problem, especially where there has been a divorce or split?

- Your children. List all their important details, perhaps include some photographs of them as babies.

- Why and when you decided to have or not to have children. Or was it a decision that was out of your hands?

- The number of children you wish you had had.

- Pregnancy(ies): highlights, worries, scares.

- What your children were like when they were born.

- How you felt about them at their birth. Not everyone bonds immediately; some mothers suffer from post-natal illnesses.

- How your feelings towards your children changed as they grew older – good and bad.

- Things you love(d) about your children.

- Things you don't/didn't like about your children.

- Magical moments or days with your children, including their birthdays and family holidays.

- Your hopes and fears for your children.

- The most wonderful things your children have said or done.

- The worst things your children have said or done: perhaps include illnesses and accidents and how you coped with them at the time.

- What you wish your children had said to you.

- What you wish you had told your children.

- Your friends' children: those you have liked and disliked.

- Children you have parented who were not your own. Was there a 'stray' who effectively became part of your family? What happened to them?

- Children you have lost, whether through miscarriage, death, divorce, migration or argument.

- Advice you gave, and would still like to give, to your children.

- What – if you are childless – you feel about not having had children.

- Worries you had about becoming a mother or father.

- How you coped with the responsibility.

- Responsibilities you passed down to the children: household chores, budgeting, having their own keys, etc.

- Rights you gave your children: the ages at which you allowed them to be more independent.

- Your children's favourite things.

- Your children's worries and fears.

- Times when your children became too much for you: how did you cope?

- How you felt about your children leaving home.

- Your grandchildren: list all their important details.

- What you feel about your grandchildren.

- What you have learned from your children and grandchildren.

- How you treated/would treat your grandchildren differently from your children.

- Your children as parents: How different/similar has their approach been to yours?

What Defines Me

'Two roads diverged in a wood, and I –
I took the one less travelled by and that
has made all the difference.'   *Robert Frost*

What might have happened if you'd made different choices? What if you had not failed that exam, taken that job, gone to live with that person, bought that house, told someone exactly what you thought of them? What if you had not broken off that engagement, not taken that holiday or stuck with that job and been promoted? This is your chance to look back and wonder.

Try to place yourself in a parallel universe where you did indeed go for the other option. Perhaps a pattern will emerge. Maybe you always took the easy option? Or the one that others felt you should take? Recalling key choices in your life and writing them down may even make you decide to alter the way you act in future. Maybe you were always slightly too careful, or too reckless and adventurous – and maybe you have paid a price for that?

Do you have the measure of yourself? What sort of person are you? How would someone else describe you? Sporty? Bookish? Thoughtful? Insecure? Considerate? Kindly? Amusing and witty? Musical? A bit of a drama queen? Life and soul? Deep? Would you have been any happier or more fulfilled if you had had different qualities? Only you can answer that question.

Take the time to record your favourite books, films and music. These may change in years to come but, as a snapshot of who you are today, right now, it is invaluable.

- **My contribution. What have you done to make *your* world a better place? Have you supported charities or worked for charities? Have you taken part in community projects? Have you been involved in politics – local or national – or campaigns?**

- **Your favourite books.**

- **Your favourite films.**

- **Your favourite music/songs.**

- **Your favourite food/types of cooking/restaurants.**

- **Your favourite TV programmes.**

- **Your favourite plays.**

- Your favourite poems.

- Your favourite paintings and or artists.

- Your favourite actors/actresses.

- Your favourite sports.

- Your heroes and heroines: not just people in the public eye but people you really admire(d).

- Your sporting achievements.

- Your collections/hobbies.

- Groups and societies of which you have been a member.

- What the world – your world – would have been like if you had never been born. Try to imagine your parents, siblings and friends without you in their midst.

- Your greatest regrets.

- Things you wish you had said or done.

- Things you wish you hadn't said or done: how would/should you have done things differently?

My Place in the World

How you deal with the wider world and the way it impinges on your life helps to determine your happiness and well-being.

Who can forget where they were on 9/11? Or the day Diana died? For anyone over the age of fifty the same can be asked of the day that President Kennedy was assassinated. These were life-changing events that spawned days of worldwide headlines and turmoil that touched each and every one of us. How do you feel about the big issues of the day?

Anyone who has lived through a war or a major conflict will remember it for the rest of his or her life. If you have, then this is the opportunity for you to record your experiences – not for public posterity but for yourself and for your family. If you lived through a period of public fear and deprivation or persecution, it's important to put it down in writing. Perhaps you or one of your family has been caught up in a national disaster like a major flood, fire, famine or tsunami. If so, it's vital to record your experience and feelings about it. But history is also in the minutiae: the first taste of a banana after years of rationing; the first time television was broadcast in colour; the days before Sunday opening.

Reflect on the difference you've made to the world around you. Explore the ramifications of your contribution and what would have happened if you hadn't joined in.

- **Where you were the day JFK was shot?**

- **Where you were when you heard Diana had died?**

- **Where you were on 9/11?**

- **How these events, or any other events of national or global importance, affected you personally and/or directly.**

- **Your political/philosophical beliefs.**

- **How your views have changed over the years.**

- **How you would solve famine and poverty.**

- **Your experience of crime and punishment.**

- Your attitude to the wider world. How tolerant are you of other people and ideas and of things alien to you?

- How you voted in each and every General Election. How, in retrospect, you wish you'd voted.

- Countries and leaders you admire or dislike.

- What you would tell the leaders of the world.

- World events that affected you at the time or later.

- If you ruled the world… what laws would you put into effect or scrap? Do you have strong views on how things ought to be done?

My Spiritual Beliefs

'When people stop believing in God, they don't believe in nothing, they believe in anything.'
G.K. Chesterton

Most people are born into some sort of organised religion. Some continue to practise that religion; others change religion or decide to forsake religion altogether. But everyone has a spiritual dimension and this is the place to explore it.

Perhaps you're a true believer and regularly attend a place of worship. Perhaps it's a side of life you've simply never had time for. If not, why not? Or you may have lost your religious identity. If so, can you identify a turning point? Even if you don't feel remotely religious, it's worth taking the time to explore your spirituality. Try to work out what it is you believe in and why you're here.

- **Your religious background. Were you born into a religious family? Were your grandparents/great grandparents religious?**

- Your christening or induction into formal religion, if you had one.

- What you learned about religion at school. How much did this inspire you or did it put you off?

- What you believed at different ages.

- How your beliefs have changed.

- How you see God.

- How you think God sees you – even if you don't believe in Him.

- The way your beliefs affect your life and the way I live it.

- Your feelings on other religions. Is there any other religion that you've been tempted to join? Or are there any that anger or repel you?

- Your philosophy of life. Why do you think we're here? Is there a grand design?

- Your spiritual/out-of-body experiences. Is there something out there? Has anything strange happened to you that can't be explained rationally?

- Near-death experiences. Do you believe in the other side? Have you or anyone you know been close enough to death to see over to the other side?

- What happens next? Do you believe in an afterlife? In reincarnation? In a spirit world? In heaven and hell? In limbo and purgatory?

- If you had just three wishes… what would you use them for?

The Final Chapter

'Life is pleasant. Death is peaceful. It's the
transition that's troublesome.'

Isaac Asimov

D eath comes to us all and while it may be
nothing to fear it still has to be planned for. For
the most part we don't know when we're going
to die and therefore it's essential to make a will.
However, there are things that wills don't tend to cover
and so this is the part of your book that, if you choose,
could help your family and friends to know precisely how
you wish to depart this life and how you want to be
remembered.

Even the people closest to you might not know which
flowers you want on your grave or what music you want
at your funeral. This is the opportunity for you to leave
them with clear instructions. In doing so, you won't only
be ensuring that everything happens just as you would
like but you'll also be giving the people close to you the
comfort that they're being true to your wishes.

There is no reason for death to be gloomy – especially if the deceased enjoyed a full life. And we live on in the hearts and minds of everyone who knew and loved us.

If you were to die suddenly would you be leaving unfinished business? Perhaps you'd like to leave behind you a note of forgiveness or apology to a friend. Perhaps you'd like to settle a score. Perhaps there's something you'd really like your loved ones to do for you after you've gone – re-visit a favourite spot, for example. Here's your chance to reveal a long held secret you wish you'd told while you still had the chance.

Alternatively, you might choose to take your book with you to the grave – unread by anyone else. If that's the case you might still want to leave a copy of this final chapter for your loved ones.

- **Your closest experience of death.**

- **How you would like to be remembered.**

- **People you would like to be informed of your death.**

- **The people you want to be at your funeral. Are there any people you specifically *don't* want to attend your funeral?**

- **The person or people you would like to make speeches or give addresses at your funeral.**

- The flowers you want at your funeral.

- The music you want at your funeral.

- The poem(s), prayer(s) or words you want said at your funeral.

- How you want your remains to be disposed of.

- Where you would like to be buried or have your ashes scattered.

- What you would like written on your tombstone.

- Your feelings on organ donation.

- The obituary you would write for yourself.

Notes